LAVENDER

NYKALE LOURIANO

MW00902368

Copyright © 2021 by Nykale Louriano

All rights reserved.

This book is an original idea written by Nykale Louriano. No parts of this book shall be duplicated, reproduced, or shared without the writer's or publisher's permission. By reading this book, you are agreeing to such terms.

Written By: Nykale Louriano

Illustration, Editing, Cover Design, and Interior Layout Design:
Kennedee Devoe/Devoe Publications

www.kdevoe.com

ISBN: 978-0-578-31022-0

Published by: Nykale Grace Publishing

Dedication

This book is dedicated to my Uncle Nate "Cheesecake" Stephens.

Acknowledgements

I would like to thank all my family for always supporting my dreams.

Lavender was a nice purple spider who was very lonely. She liked cheese crackers.

She was always teased about being different by the other, yellow spiders.

One day, she met a friend named İndigo, a spotless blue ladybug.
She liked cheese crackers as well.

She was always teased by the red ladybugs because she didn't have any spots.

Lavender and Indigo became friends.

Slither, the coolest snake in school, thought being different ruled.

He was very happy and always wanted to meet new friends.

One day, he met Indigo and Lavender. They all became friends.

When the other bugs saw how cool it was to be different, Lavender never got teased again.

Made in the USA
Coppell, TX
13 February 2022

73543101R00017